FIRST
CLASS
POSTAGE
REQUIRED

Abbeville Publishing Group • 116 West 23rd Street • New York, NY 10011

FIRST
CLASS
POSTAGE
REQUIRED

Abbeville Publishing Group • 116 West 23rd Street • New York, NY 10011

FIRST
CLASS
POSTAGE
REQUIRED

Abbeville Publishing Group • 116 West 23rd Street • New York, NY 10011

FIRST
CLASS
POSTAGE
REQUIRED

Abbeville Publishing Group • 116 West 23rd Street • New York, NY 10011

FIRST
CLASS
POSTAGE
REQUIRED

Abbeville Publishing Group • 116 West 23rd Street • New York, NY 10011

FIRST
CLASS
POSTAGE
REQUIRED

Abbeville Publishing Group • *116 West 25ʳᵈ Street* • *New York, NY 10011*

FIRST
CLASS
POSTAGE
REQUIRED

Abbeville Publishing Group • 116 West 25th Street • New York, NY 10011

Abbeville Publishing Group • 116 West 23rd Street • New York, NY 10011

Abbeville Publishing Group • 116 West 25ʳᵈ Street • New York, NY 10011

Abbeville Publishing Group • 116 West 23rd Street • New York, NY 10011

Abbeville Publishing Group • 116 West 23rd Street • New York, NY 10011

FIRST
CLASS
POSTAGE
REQUIRED

Abbeville Publishing Group • 116 West 23rd Street • New York, NY 10011

FIRST
CLASS
POSTAGE
REQUIRED

Abbeville Publishing Group • 116 West 23rd Street • New York, NY 10011

FIRST
CLASS
POSTAGE
REQUIRED

Abbeville Publishing Group • 116 West 23rd Street • New York, NY 10011

Copyright © 1994 Abbeville Press, Inc. Images copyright © Sonja Bullaty and Angelo Lomeo. Printed in Hong Kong.

Abbeville Publishing Group • 116 West 23rd Street • New York, NY 10011

FIRST
CLASS
POSTAGE
REQUIRED

Abbeville Publishing Group • 116 West 25ʳᵈ Street • New York, NY 10011

FIRST
CLASS
POSTAGE
REQUIRED

Abbeville Publishing Group • 116 West 25ʰ Street • New York, NY 10011

FIRST
CLASS
POSTAGE
REQUIRED

Abbeville Publishing Group • 116 West 23rd Street • New York, NY 10011

FIRST
CLASS
POSTAGE
REQUIRED

Abbeville Publishing Group • 116 West 23rd Street • New York, NY 10011

Abbeville Publishing Group • 116 West 25ʳᵈ Street • New York, NY 10011

Abbeville Publishing Group • 116 West 23rd Street • New York, NY 10011

Abbeville Publishing Group • 116 West 23rd Street • New York, NY 10011

FIRST
CLASS
POSTAGE
REQUIRED

Abbeville Publishing Group • 116 West 23rd Street • New York, NY 10011

Abbeville Publishing Group • 116 West 25ʳᵈ Street • New York, NY 10011

FIRST
CLASS
POSTAGE
REQUIRED

Abbeville Publishing Group • 116 West 23ʳᵈ Street • New York, NY 10011

Abbeville Publishing Group • 116 West 23rd Street • New York, NY 10011